ADOLESCENT SUICIDE

Publication Number 816

AMERICAN LECTURE SERIES®

A Monograph in

AMERICAN LECTURES IN LIVING CHEMISTRY

Edited by

I. NEWTON KUGELMASS, M.D., Ph.D., Sc.D.

*Consultant to the Department of Health and Hospitals
New York City*

ADOLESCENT SUICIDE

By

STUART M. FINCH, M.D.

Professor of Psychiatry
Director, Children's Psychiatric Hospital
Department of Psychiatry
University of Michigan Medical School
Ann Arbor, Michigan

ELVA O. POZNANSKI, M.D.

Assistant Professor of Psychiatry
Children's Psychiatric Hospital
Department of Psychiatry
University of Michigan Medical School
Ann Arbor, Michigan

With a Foreword by

Raymond W. Waggoner, M.D., Sc.D.

Professor of Psychiatry
Department of Psychiatry
University of Michigan
Ann Arbor, Michigan

CHARLES C THOMAS · PUBLISHER
Springfield · *Illinois* · *U.S.A.*

Published and Distributed Throughout the World by

CHARLES C THOMAS · PUBLISHER

BANNERSTONE HOUSE

301-327 East Lawrence Avenue, Springfield, Illinois, U.S.A.

NATCHEZ PLANTATION HOUSE

735 North Atlantic Boulevard, Fort Lauderdale, Florida, U.S.A.

© *1971, by* CHARLES C THOMAS · PUBLISHER

Library of Congress Catalog Card Number: 78-151867

With THOMAS BOOKS *careful attention is given to all details of
manufacturing and design. It is the Publisher's desire to present books
that are satisfactory as to their physical qualities and artistic possibilities
and appropriate for their particular use.* THOMAS BOOKS *will be true
to those laws of quality that assure a good name and good will.*

Printed in the United States of America

I-1

EDITOR'S FOREWORD

OUR LIVING CHEMISTRY Series was conceived by Editor and Publisher to advance the newer knowledge of chemical medicine in the cause of clinical practice. The interdependence of chemistry and medicine is so great that physicians are turning to chemistry, and chemists to medicine in order to understand the underlying basis of life processes in health and disease. Once chemical truths, proofs and convictions become sound foundations for clinical phenomena, key investigators clarify the bewildering panorama of biochemical progress for application in everyday practice, stimulation of experimental research and extension of postgraduate instruction. Each of our monographs thus unravels the chemical mechanisms and clinical management of many diseases that have remained relatively static in the minds of medical men for three thousand years. Our new Series is charged with the *nisus élan* of chemical wisdom, supreme in choice of international authors, optimal in standards of chemical scholarship, provocative in imagination for experimental research, comprehensive in discussions of scientific medicine and authoritative in chemical perspective of human disorders.

Dr. Finch and Dr. Poznanski of Ann Arbor describe suicidal attempts and suicidal threats in unstable adolescents overcome by external events repugnant to their sensitive nature. Suicide is the focus in this contribution, but the light is on life—living with frustrations, disappointments, angers, agonies and anxieties. There is much on psychological illness, its involvement in medical illness, its predominance in adolescence, its relation to sexual, educational, economic and social status. The suicidal attempt usually reflects the normal anxieties of this life period. It may be a prodromal manifestation of a serious psychotic or neurotic disorder, but as a rule it connotes a genuine appeal to others in the light of the adolescent's existential position in the modern world—the contact with reality precociously experienced under accelerated emotional pressures without parallel acceleration of psychological maturation.

Adolescent suicide rate is higher in the college than noncollege groups of the same age, but the rate is relatively constant. Apparently, the greater the intellectual freedom and the higher the intellectual level in a community, the greater the number of suicides among the socially estranged with feelings of deprivation, guilt, helplessness and rejection. Suicidal behavior is the culmination of a period of progressive adaptive decompensation. The depressed adolescent with suicidal potential usually welcomes the opportunity to discuss his own fears about his thoughts and impulses. Deep depression plus previous suicidal attempts plus coexistent long-term illness plus a family history of suicide—all increase the risk of suicide.

Suicide is a confession, not a remedy. Some cultures considered it an evil and a sin; others, a virtue; still others, the only truly serious philosophical problem. It is one of the great paradoxes of human existence, never perpetrated in an access of reasonableness during this stormy period of life with many mental breakdowns. Every case of threat or attempt should be taken seriously and investigated in the light of the personality profile, family pattern, home situation as well as the sociological, ecological and psychiatric factors involved in the youth's relationships at home, college or work. An understanding of the individual significance of the appeal inherent in the suicidal attempt would enable those who want to help, to do so rationally and effectively, to prevent repetition. The problem is always the same, but solution differs with each adolescent. It can be met only by a broad program of mental hygiene, resocialization and medical management in which psychiatric service is crucial.

We hold in our hands the power to end our sorrows,
And he who is willing to die may brave any calamity.

I. Newton Kugelmass, M.D., Ph.D., Sc.D., *Editor*

FOREWORD

A<small>T A TIME WHEN</small> the world climate is so involved with
evidences of hostility and aggression, particularly among
the alienated and rebellious youth and young adults, it is
particularly appropriate that the monograph by Finch and
Poznanski on *Adolescent Suicide* should be made available.
It is vitally important to attempt to understand the dynamics of suicide and to consider possible ways of resolving
the tensions which may lead to it. Alienation can be best
described as a sense of detachment from the values regu-
lated by society and which may, therefore, lead to non-
conformist behavior. The dimensions of alienation have
been described as powerlessness, meaninglessness, norm-
lessness, social estrangement and self-estrangement, any
one of which or a combination may lead to the kind of
reaction which will result in suicide or a suicidal attempt.
Immature individuals acting out instinctual drives may
very well be involved in homocide or suicide as a destructive action, whether this be by means of automobile or some
other source of aggressive action. It is difficult to correlate
individual psychodynamic formulations with complex social phenomenon. Ruled as we are by our unconscious and
often poorly controlled drives, it is not difficult to understand that suicide does represent a pattern of destructive
behavior.

The authors have extensively reviewed the literature
and wisely chosen material which is most appropriate in
their study. Their consideration of the suicidal act with
special reference to the precipitants and methods of suicide
are most interesting. The listing of the four categories of
suicidal types covers a wide group of problems with ap-

propriate patient examples. The discussion of various factors involved in suicide, not only those of family background and environmental factors but of other contributing elements as well, the chapter on suicide and aggressive behavior, and the chapter on suicide and the college student covertly indicate the need for further research.

It is clear as emphasized by the authors that we need to know a great deal more than we do at the present time about the various elements involved, not only in adolescent suicide, but regarding suicide at all ages. It is extremely difficult to determine whether a suicide attempt is a real one or not, and as a matter of fact, the ability to evaluate such attempts is extraordinarily difficult to describe. An important factor involved, however, is the fact that an unsuccessful suicide may very well be a desperate call for help, and this of course is particularly true where the individual declares his intent to someone who may be able to prevent the success of the suicidal attempt. The authors have presented something of the dynamics of suicide in a very effective manner.

The final chapter is particularly valuable because of the discussion of suicidal potential, the evaluation of suicide attempts, and its management. Particularly important is the reference to potentially lethal drugs and the amounts which should be prescribed at any one time.

RAYMOND W. WAGGONER

INTRODUCTION

ALL PROFESSIONAL HEALTH workers regardless of their discipline, if their work touches even peripherally on the area of mental health, are becoming increasingly concerned about the amount of emotional turmoil in our adolescents. Not only is this age group increasing in actual numbers, but they are presenting an ever greater challenge in regard to mental health. One of the important aspects of this problem is adolescent suicide.

It is fairly common knowledge that suicide in children is a comparatively rare occurrence but that the rate rises quite rapidly following puberty. This dramatic increase occurs in the ten to nineteen-year-old group. (See Tables I and II.) Needless to say, many successful suicides in teenagers could be prevented if proper mental health help were available at the time it was needed.

One of the first obligations of the professional consulted by an adolescent or his family regarding a suicide attempt is to determine the seriousness of the intent. Teenagers make many more attempts per successful suicide than do adults. The ratio for the former has been estimated as high as 120 to 1 while the adult ratio is approximately 8 to 1. Such figures could easily lead the physician or other professional into a false sense of security, especially if he is confronted by an adolescent who has made several attempts which seem to lack serious suicidal intent. It is also not uncommon for families to negate the importance of such attempts and to assume they are some form of attention-getting device or manipulative attempt.

It would seem wise to stress at this point that the emotionally healthy adolescent does not either commit suicide nor attempt to do so. One cannot escape the fact that the teen-ager who tries to kill himself is emotionally disturbed. A thorough investigation of the youngster and his family is essential, not only to provide adequate protection to those adolescents who are serious suicide risks but also proper treatment for those who have demonstrated their emotional imbalance by attempting suicide. It is the authors' intention in this monograph to attempt to give the reader a better understanding of the whole problem of adolescent suicide. We are concerned here with the magnitude of the problem, how and when teen-agers may attempt suicide, what kinds of personalities such youngsters have and what types of family patterns are found in their homes. We are also interested in social and environmental factors as well as biological influences. It is hoped that this monograph will give the professional a better understanding of the problem, how to evaluate and manage the potentially suicidal adolescent and how to assess his prognosis.

Note should be made that the major influences on suicide statistics all favor under-reporting. Some of these influences are cultural stigmas, religious taboos and the limitations of insurance policies which can combine with the family efforts to deny a suicidal intent. The awareness of the coroner's office and the police officers also influence the number of suicides reported.

TABLE 1

PER 100,000 POPULATION

0-14 Years of Age	1960	1961	1962	1963	1964	1965	1966	1967
Suicides	0.5	0.4	0.6	0.6	0.5	0.5	0.6	0.6
Males	0.9	0.7	1.0	0.9	0.9	0.9	0.9	0.9
Females	0.2	0.2	0.1	0.2	0.1	0.2	0.2	0.3
White	0.6	0.5	0.7	0.6	0.5	0.6	0.6	0.7
Males	1.0	0.7	1.1	1.0	1.0	1.0	1.1	1.0
Females	0.2	0.2	0.2	0.2	0.1	0.1	0.2	0.3
Nonwhite	0.1	0.3	0.2	0.5	0.2	0.3	0.3	0.3
Males	0.2	0.2	0.3	0.6	0.3	0.5	0.2	0.4
Females	0	0.3	0.1	0.3	0.1	0.2	0.3	0.3

Taken from Vital Statistics of the United States, Volume 2, Mortality, United States Department of Health, Education and Welfare Public Health Service.

TABLE II

PER 100,000 POPULATION

15-19 Years of Age	1960	1961	1962	1963	1964	1965	1966	1967
Suicides	3.6	3.4	3.8	4.0	4.0	4.0	4.3	4.7
Males	5.6	5.3	5.5	6.0	6.3	6.1	6.5	7.0
Females	1.6	1.5	2.0	1.9	1.7	1.9	2.1	2.4
White	3.8	3.6	3.9	4.2	4.2	4.1	4.4	4.9
Males	5.9	5.5	5.8	6.4	6.7	6.3	6.7	7.5
Females	1.6	1.6	2.0	1.9	1.7	1.8	2.1	2.2
Nonwhite	2.4	2.5	2.8	2.9	2.9	3.8	3.6	3.7
Males	3.4	3.7	3.7	3.7	4.0	5.2	4.8	3.8
Females	1.5	1.3	1.9	2.0	1.8	2.4	2.4	3.5

Taken from Vital Statistics of the United States, Volume 2, Mortality, United States Department of Health, Education and Welfare Public Health Service.

ACKNOWLEDGMENTS

THE AUTHORS HAVE been particularly fortunate in having the assistance of a number of people in this effort to present a comprehensive picture of a topic which is of rapidly increasing interest to both the lay and professional world. Their help has ranged from sharing with us some of their rich clinical experience to researching the literature and providing us with valuable editorial assistance.

We are particularly indebted to Dr. Albert C. Cain of the Department of Psychology of the University of Michigan for his willingness to share with us his vast knowledge of the literature on this topic. Helen Miranda spent many hours helping us pull together the various statistics. Drs. John Koch and Donald Schaefer deserve thanks for their assistance, particularly in the area of college mental health. Both are associated with the Student Mental Health Service at the University of Michigan. Dr. Monica Blumenthal was particularly helpful in simplifying for two clinicians some of the intricacies of the biochemistry of this topic. Dr. Lester Weiss provided guidance in the area of genetics. Drs. James McHugh and Morris Weiss, both with extensive experience in the clinical area, provided us with a broader clinical perspective.

We are also particularly indebted to Mrs. Elizabeth Killins for her painstaking editorial assistance with the manuscript. Finally, Mrs. Anita Tolen and Mrs. Betty Houston deserve thanks for the many hours spent typing and retyping the manuscript.

CONTENTS

ADOLESCENT SUICIDE

Chapter I

THE SUICIDAL ACT

PRECIPITANTS OF SUICIDAL BEHAVIOR

THE MAJORITY OF adolescents who attempt suicide do not give those people around them any signals in the form of recognizable changes in behavior that the event is forthcoming. Efforts to delineate a presuicidal syndrome in terms of behavior changes in the preceding three months prior to a suicide attempt have met with failure, except in those youngsters who are psychotic.[1] In the latter group of teenagers there did tend to be a flare-up of the psychotic symptomatology in the three months prior to the actual suicide attempt. The remainder of the adolescents studied tended to show the same general personality pattern in the study period of three months preceding the suicidal attempt. For example, the hysterical adolescent seemed no more or less hysterical in his approach to things than he had before. The impulse-ridden adolescent did not change his method of operation prior to the attempt.

The actual incidents which trigger suicidal behavior in adolescents would, on the surface, appear to be quite trivial. In most cases the attempt is a sudden, impulsive reaction to a stressful situation. Most commonly, one finds that there has been a breakup with a boyfriend or a girlfriend or a quarrel with a parent or close relative and this incident served as the immediate precipitating factor. Many of these youngsters have had suicidal ideas previously, particularly when faced with some stressful or painful situation. While further studies might clarify the role of pre-

3

cipitating events, in adolescence, the total history appears to be the most fruitful ground for investigation. One study[2] proposes the following model of behavioral stages in adolescent suicide attempts: 1) long-standing history of problems beginning in childhood; 2) a period of "escalation of problem" which generally occurred during the adolescence period and was in excess of those "normally" associated with adolescence; 3) a chain reaction dissolution of the adolescent's meaningful social relationships.

Many authors have commented on the role of sexuality in adolescent suicide attempts.[3,4,5,6] Certainly with the onset of adolescence there is a tremendous upsurge in sexual drives. The degree to which the adolescent experiences these drives varies as does his ability to handle such strong sexual emotions. Investigators have commented on the eroticized view of death commonly found in young people in contrast to the despair seen in older patients. It is not uncommon to find incestuous preoccupations in girls who attempt suicide, and in one study[6] it was estimated that one-third of the adolescent girls had actually been seduced by their fathers. In our society today there is a growing number of young teen-agers who are struggling with identity problems. On the one hand they are hopeful of eventually attaining adult masculinity or femininity, but on the other hand many forces within them resist this challenge and pull them back from it. It is almost as if they were being carried forward by a wave toward something which they fear and against which they struggle. Current cultural shifts toward blurring of sex roles may also contribute to the problem.

Another facet of the same problem is the struggle for independence in the teen-ager. He is emerging from the normal dependency of childhood and striving toward the natural independence of adulthood. He typically vacillates from dependence to independence. Suicide attempts resulting from a breakup with a friend or the loss of the love object imply the deep psychological hurt that accrues from the loss of dependency gratification. A suicidal attempt in such a situation would seem to be a regressive move as a result of the teen-ager's feelings that he can no longer depend on someone. It would indicate a desire to regress to an earlier state of security and of being cared for. Not infrequently in suicide attempts there is a sort of magical quality which reveals the hope of rejoining the lost loved one, wiping the slate clean, or affecting a rebirth after death. Such magical thinking is not uncommon in children, and in the adolescent indicates a perpetuation of earlier, more immature modes of behavior.

School difficulties are often proposed as contributing factors to adolescent suicide. If we begin with our basic assumption that any teen-ager who attempts suicide is emotionally disturbed, we could easily then hypothesize that many of them would not be doing particularly well in school. As a matter of fact, various studies[7,8,9,10,11] have indicated that those adolescents who attempt suicide have a relatively poor academic record in spite of an average IQ. A sizable percentage (estimated at even one-third) have dropped out of school for behavior rather than academic reasons. Most of these teen-agers are anywhere from one to four years behind their nonsuicidal counterparts in school. As might be expected, most of these youngsters had long-standing school problems but almost all of them had difficulties in school antedating the suicidal attempt by at least two years. It would therefore appear that school difficulties themselves are not a primary factor in the suicide attempts of most of these youngsters but rather problems which have been present for a long time and are a result of the emotional problems. It is also true that occasionally an adolescent will attempt suicide in high school or college because he finds himself unable to maintain the high standards he has set for himself and feels that he is letting everyone down, including his parents. An example is found in the child who was an honor student throughout his grade school and high school years in a small town and then entered a large university where the competition was much more difficult and he felt he could no longer achieve his compulsively high goals. Such youngsters, however, are relatively uncommon.

Contagion would appear to be a factor in some adolescent suicide attempts although this tends to occur only under particular circumstances. For example,[12,13] contagion occurs more frequently where small groups of emotionally disturbed adolescents are quartered together, in contrast to a large, state hospital situation. On occasion it has been found that a student, for example in a dormitory, may coerce another student to make a suicidal attempt only to later make one himself. It should be remembered that during adolescence group cohesiveness is a potent factor. A leader of such a group of teen-agers can often exert considerable influence over the behavior of the other members of the group. It is as if they are afraid of losing status should they not join in the particular fad. If the group leader should be preoccupied with suicidal ideas, it is not unlikely that he might coerce disturbed teen-agers into suicidal gestures even though they might not have done so on their own. Clearly, however, even such a group leader could not coerce a mentally healthy adolescent into such an activity.

METHODS OF SUICIDE

As one might suspect, the basic methods of committing suicide have remained the same for centuries. These include such methods as taking poison, shooting oneself, jumping from a high place, cutting or stabbing oneself, or being crushed, for example, jumping under an oncoming train. Many other methods could be mentioned, some new and some old; for example, suffocation by placing a plastic bag over one's head, taking an overdose of heroin, setting oneself afire with gasoline, and many other examples too numerous to mention.

It would appear that the choice of any particular method of suicide is determined both by the availability and by the cultural background of the adolescent. The majority of attempted suicides in adolescents employ some form of poisoning.[14] In completed suicides in the younger ten to fourteen-year-old group, the methods of hanging and strangulation versus firearms appeared about equally used. In the older fifteen to nineteen-year-old group, the number of successful suicides using firearms increases dramatically. The choice of method of suicide offers some broad clues to individual dynamics. For instance, psychotic adolescents tend to use more active forms of suicide such as jumping from high places. In general it can be said that males tend to use more violent methods such as guns, and women more passive methods such as poisoning. Whether this choice has a sexual basis or simply reflects the degree of desire for death is not really known. Suicide by hanging in adults in the United States tends to be more frequently employed by foreign-born individuals. This hanging reflects the cultural heritage in the choice of method in that it is a more popular method of suicide outside the United States.[15]

Mention should be made at this point of the ambivalence which is usually indicated by the suicidal patient. Most of those who attempt suicide desire both to die and at the same time to be rescued. Coroner's reports graphically describe this ambivalence in many suicide cases resulting from cutting and stabbing. The report usually indicates "hesitation marks" where obviously the individual had many qualms about what he was about to do and made many minor gestures before finally producing the fatal wound.[16] Most of us have seen newspaper pictures of a suicidal individual perched atop a building for many hours proclaiming his intent to jump and yet somehow awaiting rescue. When one compares the number of attempted suicides in adolescents to the number which succeed one can only assume this ambivalence is certainly present. If the teen-ager, naive though he may be, really wanted to kill himself, there is no question but that he could find a way to do so. We would again return to our original main point, namely, that all adolescents who attempt suicide are emotionally disturbed. Some will succeed, particularly the psychotic ones. Others will die not necessarily because they meant to, but because they misjudged what they were doing. But all of them need thorough evaluation.

REFERENCES

1. Otto, Ulf: Changes in the behavior of children and adolescents preceding suicidal attempts. *Acta Psychiat. Scand., 40*:386-400, 1964.

2. Jacobs, Jerry, and Teicher, Joseph: Broken homes and social isolation in attempted suicides of adolescent. *Int. J. Soc. Psychiat., 13*:139-149, 1967.

3. Schrut, Albert: Some typical patterns in the behavior and backgrounds of adolescent girls who attempt suicide. *Amer. J. Psychiat., 125*:69-74, 1968.

4. Mason, Percy: Suicide in adolescents. *Psychoanal. Rev., 14*:48-54, 1954.

5. Schneer, Henry I.; Kay, Paul, and Brozovsky, M.: Events and conscious ideation leading to suicidal behavior in adolescence. *Psychoanal. Quart., 35*:507-515, 1961.

6. Bigras, Julien; Gauthier, Yvon; Bouchard, Colette, and Tasse, Yolande: Suicide attempts in adolescent girls: a preliminary study. *Canad. Psychiat. Ass. J., 11*:275-282, 1966.

7. Rosenberg, Philip H., and Latimer, Ruth: Suicide attempts by children. *Ment. Hyg., 50*:354-359, 1966.

8. Otto, Ulf: Suicidal attempts made by children and adolescents because of school problems. *Acta Paediat. Scand., 54*:348-356, 1965.

9. Teicher, Joseph, and Jacobs, Jerry: Adolescents who attempt

suicide: preliminary findings. *Amer. J. Psychiat.*, *112*:1248-1257, 1966.

10. Barter, James T.; Swaback, Dwight O., and Todd, Dorothy: Adolescent suicide attempts: a follow-up study of hospitalized patients. *Arch. Gen. Psychiat.* (Chicago), *19*:523-527, 1968.

11. Schneer, Henry I., and Kay, Paul: The suicidal adolescent. In Lorand, S., and Schneer, H. T. (Eds.): *Adolescents: Psychoanalytic Approach to Problems and Therapy.* New York, Hoebler, 1961.

12. Offer, Daniel, and Barglow, Peter: Adolescent and young adult self-mutilation incidents in a general psychiatric hospital. *Arch. Gen. Psychiat.* (Chicago), *3*:194-204, 1960.

13. Binns, William A.; Kerkman, Dean, and Schroeder, Sydney O.: Destructive group dynamics: an account of some peculiar interrelated incidents of suicide and suicide attempts in a university dormitory. *J. Amer. Coll. Health Ass.*, *14*:250-256, 1966.

14. Bergstrand, C. G., and Otto, Ulf: Suicidal attempts in adolescence and childhood. *Acta Paediat. Scand.*, *51*:17-26, 1962.

15. Luke, James L.: Asphyxial deaths by hanging in New York City 1964-65. *Journal Forensic Sci.*, *12*:359-369, 1967.

16. Hirsch, Joseph: Methods and fashions of suicide, part II. *Ment. Hyg.*, *44*:3-11, 1960.

Chapter II

TYPES OF SUICIDAL ADOLESCENTS

TYPES OF SUICIDAL ADOLESCENTS

Several patterns may be identified among adolescents who attempt suicide (whether successful or not). While any attempt to categorize behavioral patterns is in itself arbitrary, it still has some usefulness. These various types can and do overlap in individual cases.

IMPULSIVE CHARACTER DISORDER

Adolescents who fall into this category represent the largest single group of teen-agers with suicidal behavior. While most of the adolescents of this type are suicide attempters, there is the occasional youngster who does complete the suicidal act. The degree of psychopathology covers a broad range and varies from the adolescent whose development has not been particularly successful and who becomes overwhelmed by adolescent sexual drives to the teen-ager whose failure to develop emotionally is so marked that the older label of "psychopathic personality" seems fitting. All of the youngsters in this group demonstrate an inability to find adequate solutions to a large number of psychological and sociological problems. The group is well represented by the angry revengeful teen-ager who tries to punish anyone who interferes with his life. These youngsters attempt to assert their independence as is typical of all adolescents but are inept in managing their independent strivings. Quite often the spiteful element in the suicide attempt is obvious and when angry, this type of teen-ager may make homicidal as well as suicidal threats. These youngsters are frequently manipulative and after a suicide attempt usually deny any serious motive. As a matter of fact, these adolescents will usually deny that they have any emotional problems at all. This, of course, is not true as subsequent crises in their lives amply demonstrate.

The following case history is fairly typical of this group of youngsters and illustrates a relative mild degree of psychopathology.

Case History: Sarah

Sarah was a tall, attractive girl seen in consultation just a few days after her sixteenth birthday following an attempted suicide, in which she had taken approximately fifty-five aspirin. After emergency treatment at a local hospital the family physician urged the parents to have Sarah see a psychiatrist. At the time of the consultation her attitude about her attempted suicide was quite casual. As she said, "It happened." She gave the impression by her evasive and shifting answers that she easily distorted information to suit her own purposes.

Sarah was the oldest of four girls and her father's favorite. He felt possessive of her, complained about her social life which frequently absented her from the family. Sarah herself did not get along well with other members of the family and complained to the psychiatrist about all of them. She was a junior in high school and did average work academically. While seeming to be very active socially she really was a fringe member of a "fast" group of youngsters. Most of them were much more experienced in heterosexual matters than she was.

On Sarah's sixteenth birthday she was allowed to date for the first time. The youngster with whom she went out was a boy whom she had secretly admired for a long time and who was much more sophisticated than she. During this date he attempted to "French kiss" her, to which she reacted by biting him. He swore at her and took her home. Her comments about the boy indicated she had been sexually aroused by him but she attempted to deny it. She said "sex" made her sick to her stomach.

The next day Sarah's parents left on a trip and it fell

her lot to be the babysitter for the younger siblings; a job she detested. It was the morning the parents left that Sarah swallowed the pills. The younger children in the family called a neighbor who contacted the parents. When the parents returned, Sarah complained about the behavior of her boyfriend on the date, describing it in some detail to her father, which, of course, mitigated some of the parental anger at having to give up their trip.

Further inquiry into Sarah's background revealed that while her adjustment looked relatively good on the surface, it was basically quite immature. She had always been a youngster who had gotten her own way in one fashion or another. Not infrequently she had turned to her father and he had always been a ready ally. She had never been prepared to stand any sort of frustration and when faced with the turmoils of adolescence she was unprepared to meet their challenge. Sarah's own sexual arousal during the date which caused panic and the wish to retreat from adult sexuality was then compounded by being left in a parent surrogate role. The result was a rise in emotional tension to the degree that attempted suicide appeared to be her only relief. The manipulative aspects of this attempt are easily seen in that it caused her parents to return home, producing a good deal of secondary gain for her.

TEEN-AGERS WITH DEPRESSIVE SYMPTOMATOLOGY

The clinical picture of a classic depression seen in adult suicides is infrequently observed in adolescents. Similarly the relationship of depression to suicidal behavior in adolescents is less clear than it is with adults. Typically, teen-agers display markedly fluctuating moods; an exaggeration of which is often apparent in emotionally disturbed adolescents. Because of these fluctuations, periods of obvious depression in adolescents can be easily missed. The depressed teen-ager often reveals social withdrawal, loss of initiative, a decrease in appetite, and difficulty sleeping. Investigators of adolescent suicide attempters[1,2] found depressive symptoms in approximately 40 per cent of their series. One author[3] has suggested that depression is higher in adolescent suicides but goes unrecognized. He feels that behavioral equivalents of depression exist, such as truancy, disobedience, and self-destructive behavior.

A fairly common type of depression in adolescents is that which represents the expression of grief, either acute or prolonged, over the loss of the loved one. In such a youngster the overt depression is accompanied by a pervasive sense of loneliness. Such loneliness is further contributed to by the large size and impersonal methods of operation of many of our high schools and universities.

Another type of depressed adolescent is the one who has marked a self-depreciating attitude. He sees himself as "the bad one." His wish to die is an ambivalent desire to punish himself and to prove his "goodness" to others. The hostility in this type of thinking as well as the hostility seen in the lives of such adolescents is very thinly disguised, if at all. Occasionally the adolescent girl attempts to "undo" her promiscuity by a suicide attempt.

Teen-agers with depressive symptomatology often have characterological problems as well and hence can easily be confused with the impulsive character disorder. The following case history exemplifies both characterological and depressive symptomatology.

Case History: Sue

Only a few sketchy facts are known about Sue's early life. At two months of age she and her three-year-old brother were deserted by their mother. For the next three years the youngsters were cared for jointly by the father and paternal grandparents. During this time the father attempted unsuccessfully to obtain legal custody of the youngsters from the grandfather. After his efforts failed, the father vanished from their life and subsequently visited them a total of three times in the ensuing years. From ages three to nine years, Sue was raised by the paternal grandfather with a step-grandmother entering the scene at an unknown point. Sue's emotional problems were apparent in grade school where it was reported that she would have rage reactions, set fires, break windows, and loudly proclaim her hatred for her brother. Further difficulty developed for Sue with the death of her grandfather when she was nine years old. She did not get along well with the step-grandmother and soon after the loss of her grandfather she ran away from home and complained to police about the grandmother's cruelty to her. Approximately a year later a neglect petition was filed against the grandmother but was subsequently dismissed. The court commented at that time on the poor living conditions for two children ages ten and thirteen years. Sue tried to get her grandmother's attention and sympathy in many ways, including at-attempted suicide appeared to be her own relief. The manipu-incident, the grandmother did not believe that Sue actually had swallowed the pins and refused to take her to a hospital. An uncle finally intervened and obtained medical care for her.

Her difficulties in school escalated. She constantly felt picked on by all her friends and frequently was involved in fights. At age twelve she got into a particularly serious altercation at school and had to be physically restrained to prevent her from doing serious damage to another child. Because of this incident the school referred her for psychological testing. When asked by the psychologist during testing what would make her happy, she replied, "Death." The psychological report indicated that she was "seriously depressed and suicidal."

A few months later Sue swallowed many pills and was again taken to a hospital. She stated that she had done it because her friends were "mad" at her. From the hospital she was committed to a mental institution and the second neglect petition was filed against the step-grandmother. Sue remained in the state hospital for one year during which time she behaved relatively well. The full extent of her psychopathology not being revealed in this very structured environment, she was diagnosed as having a personality disorder and as not "mentally ill." The hospital staff suggested that Sue be made a ward of the court and sent to a foster home.

Sue was released from the mental hospital, admitted to a boarding home and soon thereafter attempted to burn it down, ending her first placement. A second placement was equally unsuccessful. In the third placement the boarding mother tried particularly hard to reach her but Sue ran away relatively soon after arriving. A fourth and last boarding home placement was attempted, this one in the home where her brother lived next door. Soon after entering this foster home an argument began between Sue and the foster parents and the youngster broke down the kitchen door with a hammer and swallowed two bottles of pills. She was removed from this foster home and sent to a group placement for delinquent teen-agers.

Sue's adjustment in the group placement was stormy. She refused to conform to rules, flew into rages, broke windows, swore loudly and on several occasions tried to take overdoses of pills.

She was seen in psychiatric consultation four months after entering a group placement. She appeared as a mildly overweight, black teenager with prominent Negroid features. She stated that she was fifteen years old although the record indicated that she was actually fourteen. Her mood during the interview was one of mild depression which fluctuated, and she occasionally smiled.

She described her attempts to get her grandmother's attention without enthusiasm. When asked who she felt closest to her facial expression was one of complete bewilderment. She finally answered, "My father." Considering the lack of involvement of the father with Sue this answer appeared to be a desperate attempt to create a family. Psychological testing indicated an average IQ. On projective testing Sue appeared emotionally out of control, felt "stupid" and "rotten," rejected, abandoned, and worthless. Affectively she was extremely labile, showed great anger and a deep sense of hurt. She was still reaching out for human relationships but found them of little gratification. There were many infantile elements to her personality and strong dependency needs were quite apparent. During the testing when given the key word "death" and asked to fill in the rest of the sentence Sue responded by saying, "It is in the family."

Although Sue was never accepted by her peers, she continued in the group placement for several more months. After Christmas she became more depressed and began telling some of the girls in the cottage that they were going to die on a certain date. This tactic proved unnerving both for the girls and the staff. One evening Sue became extremely angry and went to the cottage parents claiming she was being picked on by all the other youngsters, and screamed profanities. The episode culminated when she swallowed a safety pin.

Plans were made for a second psychiatric evaluation. The day prior to this reevaluation, Sue told some of her friends that she had safety pins hidden and planned to swallow them and kill herself. She also told them that her ghost would haunt all of the girls that night. This frightened the other youngsters sufficiently for them to ask to have their doors locked at night. That evening Sue seemed to be "high" and in a state of excitement and agitation. She began causing minor disturbances which snowballed when she became more and more out of control. In the heat of her anger she screamed at the cottage staff, "I'll kill myself right in front of you." She was removed from the main cottage to a discipline room for the night. An hour later when the staff came by to check her she was dead. She had hung a towel around the toilet and asphyxiated herself.

PSYCHOTIC TEEN-AGER

Roughly 16 per cent of all adolescents who attempt suicide are diagnosed as psychotic. The largest number of them are schizophrenic, with a smaller number diagnosed as manic-depressive psychosis. Boys out-number girls more than two to one.[4] There are two reasons why this group of youngsters comprise a most serious and difficult challenge. In the first place, their behavior is unpredictable and in the second place they tend to use more active methods in their suicide attempts. These are often adolescents who are delusional and withdrawn, spending a great deal of time daydreaming or living in a fantasy world. These mentally ill adolescents are more apt than other suicidal teenagers to give some clue ahead of time in the form of an observable change in behavior. Even so, only about 50 per cent of them do undergo this personality change during the three months preceding their suicidal attempt. Studies of these patients indicate that they are actively and overtly mentally ill at the time of the suicide attempt with paranoid and catatonic types being most frequently encountered.[5]

The psychotic adolescent who attempts suicide generally has less external and observable reasons for the suicide attempt than does his nonpsychotic counterpart. The relationship between depression and schizophrenia, relative to suicide, is unclear. A stronger relationship appears to exist between psychosis and suicide. This is not to say the psychotic adolescent cannot be depressed, but simply depression cannot be the hallmark of suicide potential for any adolescent.

From the statistical standpoint the risk of suicide is the greatest during the first year of the mental illness or during an acute psychotic episode. While at times it may be easy to diagnose the onset of a psychotic break because of the florid nature of the symptoms, at other times it is much more difficult. For example, a teen-ager may sit quietly in his room listing to himself in his own mind the wrongs done to him by his parents, siblings, peers, and others. He becomes increasingly desperate but does not share his own inner turmoil with anyone around him. A quote from the diary of a fourteen-year-old boy a few days before he killed himself illustrates this tragically and poetically: "Why? Why must others do this to me? I have done nothing to them. I have not harmed them. I was merely born . . ." In his diary, which he shared with no one, he vividly described the chaos in his mind along with his desperate attempts to clear his thinking. He was slowly being alienated from all people, save one friend whom he worshiped idealistically. Near the end of his diary he wrote "to some this thing I do will be just a name in the newspaper, to others it will mark the end of an era," suggesting some psychotic grandiosity. Suicide in some acutely disturbed adolescents may be a reaction of the intact part of personality to their own psychosis.

In summary, the psychotic adolescent represents an

extremely difficult challenge, especially from the standpoint of suicidal potential. Perhaps half of them will show some behavioral changes in the three months prior to their suicide attempt but the other half will not. When they do attempt suicide it is more apt to be by an active method, and not triggered by any particular environmental event. On occasion they will verbalize or in some other fashion indicate their suicidal intentions, but in many instances this does not take place and no warning is given. Finally, the suicidal risk is greatest in the early stages of the psychosis which may or may not be recognized by the family or others.

WRIST CUTTING SYNDROME

In some respects the wrist cutting syndrome is a variant of the psychotic pattern. It has been called a syndrome because there appear to be similarities within the patient group above and beyond the act of wrist slashing. In studies[6,7] of these patients the majority are young females, of whom about half are under twenty.[6] They show intense loneliness, boredom and poor social relationships. In two series which have been reported they have had a higher than average IQ. The diagnosis is usually that of borderline syndrome or schizophrenia. A few of them have been diagnosed as character disorders. The wrist slashing itself is rarely life threatening but would appear to serve as a means of reducing the tension of the individual and at the same time serving as a source of pleasure. One of the distinguishing features may be the attitude of the patient towards blood and cutting. Some authors have felt that it was a desperate attempt on the part of the patient to avoid depersonalization and psychosis, and that the act of wrist cutting relieved the depersonalized state.[8] The following case history illustrates this type of patient.

Case History: Beth

Beth was a fourteen-year-old girl in the ninth grade who

was referred to the psychiatrist after she had slashed her wrists on three separate occasions, each following a breakup with a boyfriend. Her chief complaint at the time of the interview was, "I want to die." On one occasion after slashing her wrist, she had stayed up all night to watch it bleed with curious fascination.

During the psychiatric interview it became increasingly evident that Beth was an extremely disturbed youngster with many borderline psychotic features. She had difficulty sleeping and when she finally did go to sleep she would often awake "in a cold sweat." All of her relationships seemed to have a strong sadomasochistic tinge and there was little evidence that she had ever had a reasonably normal relationship with anyone. The boyfriend that she had broken up with prior to her latest wrist slashing episode was described by her as someone she wanted to be close to and physically intimate with. Their relationship had, in fact, been quite brief and tumultuous. On one occasion her boyfriend had hit her with his fist, causing a laceration which required seven stitches. Beth apparently considered this an unimportant event, but her attitude indicated the primitive nature of her relationships. She was a youngster who had an unusual number of masculine interests and obviously had many difficulties with her sexual identity. When treated with tranquilizers she became quite comfortable and shortly thereafter announced that she no longer wanted to see a psychiatrist because "there is nothing wrong with me."

REFERENCES

1. Otto, Ulf: Changes in the behavior of children and adolescents preceding suicidal attempts. *Acta Psychiat. Scand.*, *40*:386-400, 1964.
2. Mattsson, Ake; Seese, Lynne R., and Hawkins, James W.: Suicidal behavior as a child psychiatric emergency. *Arch. Gen. Psychiat.*, *20*:100-109, 1969.
3. Toolan, James M.: Suicide and suicidal attempts in children and adolescents. *Amer. J. Psychiat.*, *118*:719-724, 1962.
4. Otto, Ulf: Suicidal attempts made by psychotic children and adolescents. *Acta Paediat. Scand.*, *56*:349-356, 1967.

5. Balser, Benjamin H., and Masterson, James F.: Suicide in adolescents. *Amer. J. Psychiat.,* 116:400-404, 1959.
6. Graff, Harold, and Mallin, Richard: The syndrome of the wrist cutter. *Amer. J. Psychiat.,* 124:36-42, 1967.
7. Rinzler, Carl, and Shapiro, David A.: Wrist cutting and suicide. *J. Mount Sinai Hospital,* 35:485-488, 1968.
8. Rosenthal, Richard J.; Rinzler, Carl; Wallsh, Rita, and Klausner, Edmund: Wrist cutting syndrome: the meaning of a gesture. APA Convention, San Francisco, 1970.

Chapter III
SOME ASPECTS OF THE FAMILY BACKGROUND

It is reasonable to ask what kinds of family backgrounds the suicidal adolescent patient has. Some indication of the range of family pathology is seen from the preceding chapter.

Studies of parental attitudes of families of adolescent suicide attempters are primarily descriptive and impressionistic. For instance, in one study[1] the mothers of adolescent girls who attempted suicide were described as "cold, rejecting, and rigid," a description which could be given of mothers of many nonsuicidal psychiatric patients. Still another study of adolescent boys[2] describes the mothers as "angry, depressed, and withdrawn," and this also could be a description of many mothers of psychiatric patients. In the latter study, the mothers were often preoccupied with their own depression and pushed their sons to assume the role of husbands. Both studies showed the fathers to be passive, weak, rejecting, or absent. Such phrases are truly impressionistic and could be widely quoted for mothers and fathers of many kinds of patients. They do, however, indicate a certain amount of parental pathology within the families of these adolescent suicide attempters.

Certainly the parental attitudes toward these youngsters has been described correctly as one of intense ambivalence.[3] This concept was made even more clear when Sabbath[4] coined the term *the expendable child*. It was his feeling that at least half of the parents of these youngsters had conveyed the attitude to their children that they were a burden and they really wished these youngsters had not been born. The adolescent suicidal behavior may be the direct expression of the unconscious wishes of the rest of the family. It is not unusual to find the suicide attempt triggered by a parental remark of "drop dead" or "you're a pain to have around." Following a suicide attempt, a family's inability to take the matter seriously or to remember to remove drugs and/or lethal weapons from the house highlight the ways unconscious hostility may be expressed by the family. Successful suicide may relate both to the family's hostility and to the victim's inability to retaliate.[5] Most investigators have tended to reach somewhat the same conclusion, namely, that there is a deprivation of love which in turn leads to increased aggressiveness and depression as well as sadomasochistic attitudes on the part of the youngsters.

A relatively few studies have focused on the early childhood patterns of adolescents who later attempted suicide. Statistically these youngsters were more likely born into large families[6] and were either the first born or perhaps the youngest in the family.[6,7,8,9] One could easily guess at some of the reasons for such statistics. For example, in some large families many of the children may not have been wanted and were thus given less than their fair share of love and attention. As far as firstborns are concerned, many young parents are unprepared to take care of children and only gradually learn this with subsequent children. Epidemiological studies of psychiatric clinics and hospitals have a disproportionate number of firstborns. Thus, emotional disturbance is again linked to suicidal behavior. Finally, as far as the youngest in the family is concerned, this would perhaps be the child who is most apt to be not wanted and not planned.

While it is true that the majority of younger children have at some time had transitory thoughts of suicide[10] these thoughts themselves are not necessarily evidence of emotional disturbance. Of primary importance is the action taken by the youngster on such thoughts and the general behavior pattern which may give evidence of potential self-destructiveness. For example, we not infrequently see children who repeatedly injure themselves, take unnecessary chances, seem heedless to danger and who, if they keep these acts up, may well be killed.

Early childhood behavior patterns of adolescent suicide attempters has shown that depressive and self-destructive behavior continues.[3] Schrut feels that there are two groups of youngsters: 1) the quietly withdrawn, chronically depressed child who is likely to have an overtly rejecting mother and 2) the anxious, "difficult to handle" never satisfied child whose mother is likely to become more ambivalent as the child becomes older. This child, in turn, shows increasingly aggressive, hostile, and delinquent behavior. This study correlates with Lester's study[11] which indicated that the behavior of suicidal subjects tends to display increasing irritability and resentment in contrast to his control subjects. Children often utilize suicidal threats as a play around which further provocation and counter-provocation will occur. As they enter latency and early adolescence they tend to have a poor identification with their own biological sexual role. The stage is then set for fits of depression, delinquent behavior, and poor social relationships.

Most studies show that, in general, suicidal teenagers come from families characterized by disorganization, parental disharmony, cruelty, abandonment, dependency, and delinquency. Since we know the needs of the psychological apparatus of the growing youngster, it is no wonder that if he is given this type of environment, he is more apt to become self-destructive.

One of the more important relationships appears to be between parental loss, broken homes, and subsequent suicide. This relationship has been documented in many studies. However, the subtleties of the relationship within these factors have been difficult to tease out. Neurotics have a high incidence of broken homes and marital disharmony in their own parental background. Hence, studies are particularly vulnerable to the type of control population used. For example, if a control population is taken from the population at large, discrepancies between it and the attempted suicide group may be great. The population group has a relatively small number of people who have had severe emotional disorders. When a controlled population is taken from a mental hospital group the difference between it and the attempted suicide group becomes narrower. It does appear that the group of attempted suicides have slightly more broken homes and parental loss than a group of mental hospital patients without suicidal behavior. However, it becomes apparent that other social factors are exceedingly important, i.e. whether there has been a recent death of a family member, having all the implication of bereavement and the difficulties of finding a satisfactory parental substitute, unemployment, residential mobility, and marital disharmony.

Some authors have focused on the type of parental separation but comparison of studies is difficult because of the differing definitions of what actually constitutes a separation; i.e. does the parent have to be totally out of the home for six to twelve months or is occasional visiting still equivalent to a parental separation? The hypothesis that suicide attempters have been separated either in a more traumatic fashion or at an earlier age than a similar nonsuicidal group has been put forth but as yet the relationship is not well documented.

The importance of parental loss in the etiology of suicidal behavior in adults has been well described. While studies of adults are useful they cannot be directly transcribed to the adolescent. One study[12] comparing attempted suicide versus completed suicide revealed that divorce was the most common cause of a broken home in those who attempted suicide, in contrast to the group who completed suicide where loss of a parent by death was more frequent. In this study, however, even intact homes showed a high incidence of marital disharmony. The one exception was the schizophrenic group who were more likely to have come from an intact home. Another investigator[13] attempted to define the type of parental loss in attempted suicide by the following method. He compared a group of attempted suicides with a group of psychiatric outpatients, matching sex, and social class. The loss of both parents was four times as common in the attempted suicide group. He found that for those who attempted suicide, the loss of the parent was "irreversible," such as by death or divorce, whereas, in the nonsuicidal control group any parental absence from the home tended to be temporary and on the basis of emergency such as war, local unemployment, imprisonment, or chronic hospitalization. These studies on attempted suicide groups go in the same direction as those which have correlated adult depression with parental loss.

There have been many attempts made to relate parental loss during childhood to subsequent suicidal attempts in adults. These have resulted in conflict findings about the significance of losing a mother or a father. One investigator[14] feels the loss of the father more important, and others[15,16,17] suggested that the loss of either parent is quite significant. Attempts have been made to correlate the age at which the parental loss occurred with later suicidal behavior.

It is difficult to define the loss of one parent, since such a loss invariably affects the relationships of the remaining family members. For example, if the father leaves the family by death or desertion, the mother may need to return to work. The children may technically be defined as having suffered the loss of their father while in reality they lose both their father and part of their mother. Levi[18] feels parental loss is more significant, if it occurs between birth and seven years. He found the number of such separations higher in parents of his suicide attempt group than in the control group. He concluded "multiple rather than single childhood separations may be of importance in determining the vulnerability to suicide attempts." Dorpat[19] correlated suicidal behavior with loss of a parent before the eighteenth birthday.

The importance of parental loss and broken homes in adolescent emotional disturbances is illustrated by the studies of Bruhn.[16,20] In studies of mixed age groups including both adolescents and adults, broken homes appeared more significant in the younger suicides. Investigators[7,21,22,23] reveal a range of 44-66 per cent of broken homes in adolescent suicide attempters; however, these figures can be used to convey a general impression as studies using adequate control populations are rare. As Bruhn has shown, far more than the fact of a broken home is involved in subsequent adolescent suicidal attempts. A slightly higher percentage who have suffered these previous losses do attempt suicide, but many other factors which have not been thoroughly studied are involved. The age at the parental loss takes place by death or desertion (usually a result of marital disharmony) is likely important. The degree of identification between the child and lost parent may be reflected in patterns of depression and suicidal behavior which originated from the missing parent. The stability of the remaining parent and the availability of relatives to partially fill parental roles would logically seem significant. The style of the family in handling feelings of frustration and aggression are also determining factors.

It would seem to us that a stable parental marital situation markedly lessens the likelihood of attempted suicide in youngsters. There are certainly adolescents who attempt suicide even though their parents have remained together, while others do not attempt suicide even though they have lost a parent or experienced a parental divorce. However, it would appear that family disunity, multiple separations, and divorces enhance the possibility of such suicidal attempts. Statistical variations between multiple or single separations, between divorces and separations, and other such items would appear less important than the fact that family upheavels have taken place. In addition to this, the way in which the death of a parent was handled, the divorce was arranged, the separations were entered into, and many other factors are of course relevant.

It is obvious that the psychological implications of a broken home for an adolescent are multiple. Such a broken home can produce feelings of emotional desertion with the adolescent mourning the loss, or feeling at least the loss of a meaningful relationship. There are inherent difficulties in a one-parent family.[24] Not infrequently the children overidealize the departed parent and the sexual identity of the child in this situation is impeded by the reality of having but one parent. Sexual identity is achieved not only by identification with the same sexed parent but also by the reciprocal male-female responses occurring with the relationship of the child to the opposite-sexed parent. Therefore the loss of either the same or opposite sexed parent complicates the achievement for the child of a solid sexual identity. Often, children from one-parent families, when they reach adolescence, get into serious disagreements with the remaining parent. In addition the adolescent from a one-parent family is faced with social dilemmas of explaining his home situation to his peers. Often, reticence to discuss these problems cuts off the more usual intense adolescent-peer relationships which facilitate separation emotionally from the parent and ultimately maturity. Another difficulty is that young people in separated families are often forced into positions of undue responsibility much too early.

Remarriage and step-parents are important factors. One

study showed that 58 per cent of the parents of suicide
attempts remarried compared to 25 per cent of the control group adolescents.[25] The 25 per cent control parents
which did remarry, did so early in the lives of their
youngsters and, in general, tended to remain married. On
the other hand, parents of suicide attempters remarried
later or if they remarried earlier were divorced and remarried several times more. This serves to illustrate the damag-
ing effects of continued family instability.

Another indication of family instability in such cases
is shown by the number of contacts with social agencies
made by these families. Adolescent suicide families have
significantly increased number of contacts with social agencies.[21] These contacts were made in diminishing order of
frequency for the reasons of delinquency, poor domestic
relations, health, economic and lastly, psychiatric disorders.
In another study[26] 29 per cent of the home situations were
so poor that intervention by the Society for the Prevention
of Cruelty to Children was sought.

Despite the multiple evidence of family instability and
its correlation with adolescent suicide attempts, there would
not appear to be sufficient data to correlate the actual degree of family disorganization and social disruption with
a greater risk of serious suicidal behavior. Certainly we
know that many parents remain together, do not separate
or get divorced and give a superficial evidence of com-
patibility while their children eventually attempt suicide.

Certainly when a family member suicides there are
reverberations throughout the rest of the family and much
rumination occurs as to each one's possible contribution.
It is not unusual to find a postsuicidal pattern in which
one or another are self-destructive following the suicide
of one member.[27] Hence, one suicide within a family may
contribute to further suicide attempts within any one
family.

REFERENCES

1. Bigras, Julien; Gauthier, Yvon; Bouchard, Colette, and Tassé, Yolande: Suicidal attempts in adolescent girls: a preliminary study. *Canad. Psychiat. Ass. J.*, *11*:275-282, 1966.
2. Margolin, N. Lionel, and Teicher, Joseph D.: Thirteen adolescent male suicide attempts: dynamic considerations. *J. Amer. Acad. Child Psychiat.*, *7*:296-315, 1968.
3. Schrut, Albert: Suicidal adolescents and children. *JAMA*, *188*:1103-1107, 1964.
4. Sabbath, Joseph C.: The suicidal adolescent—the expendable child. *J. Amer. Acad. Child Psychiat.*, *8*:272-289, 1969.
5. Rosenbaum, Milton, and Richman, Joseph: Suicide: the role of hostility and death wishes from the family and significant others. *Amer. J. Psychiat.*, *126*:128-131, 1970.
6. Haider, Ijaz: Suicidal attempts in children and adolescents. *Brit. J. Psychiat.*, *114*:1133-1134, 1968.
7. Toolan, James: Suicide and suicidal attempts in children. *Amer. J. Psychiat.*, *118*:719-724, 1962.
8. Lawler, Robert H.; Nakielny, Wladyslaw, and Wright, Nancy A.: Suicide attempts by children. *Canad. Med. Ass. J.*, *89*:751-754, 1963.
9. Perlstein, Abraham P.: Suicide in adolescence. *New York J. Med.*, *66*:3017-3020, 1968.
10. Lourie, Reginald S.: Suicide and attempted suicide in children and adolescents. *Texas Med.*, *63*:58-63, 1967.
11. Lester, David: Attempted suicide as a hostile act. *J. Psychol.*, *68*:243-248, 1968.
12. Dorpat, Theodore L.; Jackson, Joan K., and Ripley, Herbert S.: Broken homes and attempted and completed suicides. *Arch. Gen. Psychiat.*, *12*:213-216, 1965.
13. Greer, Steven: The relationship between parental loss and attempted suicide: a control study. *Brit. J. Psychiat.*, *110*:698-705, 1964.
14. McConaghy, N.; Linane, J., and Buckle, R.: Parental deprivation and attempted suicide. *Med. J. Aust.*, *1*:886-892, 1966.
15. Koller, K. M., and Castonos, J.: The influence of childhood parental deprivation in attempted suicide. *Med. J. Aust.*, *1*:396-399, 1968.

16. Bruhn, John G.: Broken homes among attempted suicides and psychiatric outpatients: a comparative study. *J. Ment. Sci.*, *108*:772-779, 1962.

17. Greer, Steven: Parental loss and attempted suicide: a further report. *Brit. J. Psychiat.*, *112*:465-470, 1966.

18. Levi, L. David; Fales, Catherine H.; Stein, Marvin, and Sharp, Vernon H.: Separation and attempted suicide. *Arch. Gen. Psychiat.*, *15*: 158-164, 1966.

19. Dorpat, Theodore, and Ripley, Herbert S.: A study of suicide in the Seattle area. *Compr. Psychiat.*, *1*:349-359, 1960.

20. Bruhn, John, and McCulloch, Wallace: Paternal deprivation among attempted suicides. *Brit. J. Psychiat.*, *6*:186-191, 1962.

21. Barter, James T.; Swaback, Dwight O., and Todd, Dorothy: Adolescent suicide attempts: a follow-up study of hospitalized patients. *Arch. Gen. Psychiat.*, *19*:523-527, 1968.

22. Jacobziner, Harold: Attempted suicides in adolescents by poisoning. *J. Psychotherapy*, *19*:247-252, 1965.

23. Bergstrand, C. G., and Otto, Ulf: Suicidal attempts in adolescence and childhood. *Acta Paediat. Scand.*, *51*:17-26, 1962.

24. Neubauer, Peter B.: The one-parent child and his oedipal development. *Psychoanal. Stud. Child*, *15*:286-309, 1960.

25. Jacobs, Jerry, and Teicher, Joseph: Broken homes and social isolation in attempted suicides. *Int. J. Soc. Psychiat.*, *13*:139-149, 1967.

26. Tuckman, Jacob, and Connon, Helen E.: Attempted suicide in adolescents. *Amer. J. Psychiat.*, *119*:228-232, 1962.

27. Cain, Albert, and Fast, Irene: Children's disturbed reactions to parent suicide. *Amer. J. Orthopsychiat.*, *36*:873-880, 1966.

Chapter IV

ENVIRONMENTAL FACTORS IN SUICIDE

THE FREQUENCY of suicide is related to a widely diverse group of sociological factors. For instance, there are suggestive trends that it is more frequent in urban than in rural communities.[1] It is also more frequent in shifting communities than in stable communities.[2] A higher incidence of suicide correlates with overcrowded conditions, children in foster homes or boarding care, a high rate of secondary school absenteeism, broken homes, and juvenile delinquency.[3]

A hypothesis put forward by Henry and Short[4] led to the popular conclusion that high social status and suicide were related. However, later reports[5,1] have repudiated this hypothesis and, in fact, found that there is a higher suicide rate among persons of the lower socioeconomic groups. However, it should be borne in mind that this is only a crude generalization and does not take into account individual family stability. In addition, it would appear that loss of status may relate more significantly to suicide than status position itself.

In the past, the black population has had a considerably lower suicide rate than has the white population and while it is still somewhat lower, it is rising rapidly at the present time. Females are also showing a current increase in the number of completed suicides. All of these statistics would seem to indicate that social change affecting status in the community is reflected in the suicide rate.

There are occasional sociological variables which affect

the adult suicide rate in one direction while affecting the adolescent's rate in the opposite direction. For instance, an English study[6] showed during the years of World War II adult suicides declined while adolescent suicides increased. Adolescent suicides, however, do tend to show a seasonal variation. In the United States they are highest in the spring[8] but it is interesting to note that in Sweden they are highest in November.[1] The time of day most frequently selected by adolescents to commit suicide is from three o'clock in the afternoon to midnight,[9] in contrast to adults who more frequently successfully suicide in the early morning.

Cultural factors are also known to play a significant role in the frequency of suicide in adolescent and adult groups. Both religious and ethnic factors are important. For example, in most communities, Catholics have a lower suicide rate than Protestants. However Catholicism does not always provide a powerful deterrent against suicide, for example the predominantly Catholic Puerto Ricans in New York have a high rate of suicide. Such figures indicate some of the difficulties in attempting to generalize regarding any one sociocultural factor and its influence on suicide.

There have been many attempts to correlate the frequency of suicide with weather conditions. Perhaps this is because of a natural tendency for most people to enjoy a sunny day and perhaps feel slightly depressed on a grey, cloudy day. However, careful studies have failed to show any relationship between suicide and weather.[7]

REFERENCES

1. Bergstrand, C. G., and Otto, Ulf: Suicidal attempts in adoescence and childhood. *Acta Paediat. Scand., 51*:17-26, 1962.
2. Cavan, Ruth: *Suicide.* New York, Russell and Russell, 1965.
3. McCulloch, J. W.; Philip, A. E., and Carstairs, G. M.: Ecology of suicidal behavior. *Brit. J. Psychiat., 9*:30-36, 1967.
4. Henry, Andrew F., and Short, James F.: *Suicide and Homicide:*

Some Economic, Sociological Aspects of Aggression. Glencoe, Free Press, 1954.

5. Lukianowicz, N.: Attempted suicide in children. *Acta Psychiat. Scand., 44*:415-435, 1968.

6. Mulcock, Donald: Juvenile suicide. *Med. Officer, 94*:155-160, 1955.

7. Pokorny, Alex; Davis, Fred, and Harberson, Wayne: Suicide, suicide attempts and weather. *Amer. J. Psychiat., 120*:377-381, 1963.

8. Jacobziner, Harold: Attempted suicides in children. *J. Pediat. 56*:519-525, 1960.

9. Tuckman, Jacob, and Connon, Helen E.: Attempted suicide in adolescents. *Amer. J. Psychiat., 119*:228-232, 1962.

Chapter V
ADDITIONAL RELATED FACTORS

BIOCHEMICAL CORRELATES

W E ARE BEGINNING to accumulate considerable evidence for a biochemical basis for affective depression. The ability of certain substances such as adrenocortical steroids and reserpine-type drugs to produce depression and the effectiveness of electroshock therapy, as well as anti depressive drugs, to diminish depression has added impetus to the study of the biochemistry of this disorder. More recently, the use of lithium in the treatment of mania along with many other observations has focused increased attention on the electrolyte changes which occur in depression. The exact biochemical mechanisms are still unclear, but would appear to relate to indoyl-metabolism and electrolytes.[1] While the research in this field is fascinating, it unfortunately has little practical application at this time, except for the studies about drug effects and drug dosages.

INHERITANCE

An important investigation of the possible genetic factors in suicide was done by Kallmann.[2] This study was based upon seventeen twin suicide cases of which six came from the literature. The author concluded that suicide was not genetically determined on the basis of his studies. However, since the entire study utilized only a small number of subjects it is not conclusively proven, and therefore, needs further validation. One might anticipate in a larger study, that twins, usually raised in the same environment, might commit suicide slightly more frequently, since they would obviously be subject to similar emotional and environmental difficulties. It would however be necessary to obtain identical twins raised in different homes in order to sort out genetic and environmental factors.

Some work has been done on the genetics of depression which can be indirectly related to suicide. Manic-depressive illness, of all of the various types of depression, most clearly appears to have some hereditary elements. Neurotic depression has been linked to an increased risk of manic-depressive illness in relatives[3] suggesting a possible but perhaps distant relationship between endogenous and neurotic depression.

SUICIDE AND MENSTRUATION

There appears to be an association between suicide and menstruation. This was shown by the statistics indicating a larger number of suicide attempts during the premenstrual or menstrual period. While the premenstrual and menstrual increase is the more common pattern, occasionally it is found that a woman has a marked midmenstrual cycle fluctuation in mood which is reflected in a small number of suicide attempts at mid-cycle.[4,5] The increase in suicide attempts premenstrually and menstrually suggests that a physiological condition may be at least a contributing factor to the suicide attempt. It should be remembered, however, that the relationship beween suicide and menstruation is only one of many such associations. Menstruation has also been correlated with an increase in psychotic symptomatology, admission rates to mental hospitals, accidents and criminal behavior. It is also interesting to note that such monthly behavioral disturbances have been shown to begin even prior to the menarche.

Premenstrual suicide attempts have some common characteristics. They are more apt not to be premeditated and more prone to be precipitated by some type of quarrel. Premenstrual suicide attempts occur significantly more often in women who are living with a mate.[6] It would appear, therefore, that emotional stress escalates premenstrual tension.[4] One could certainly put this the other way around; namely, that premenstrual tension escalates emotional stress. We still have a great deal to learn about the interrelationships between endocrines, autonomics, and the psyche.

SUICIDES DURING PREGNANCY

Whitlock and Edwards[7] have stated that pregnancy is an associated factor in approximately 5 per cent of all female suicides and that about 7 per cent of women who commit suicide are pregnant. This latter figure closely approximates the percentage of women pregnant during childbearing years. The time of the suicide attempt is generally during the second and third month.[8] For this reason statistics are somewhat difficult to obtain and an abortion attempt may be disguised as a suicide attempt.

The pregnancy itself is generally not the cause of the suicide attempt but rather the result of violent interpersonal disputes.[7] Women whose suicide attempts were during pregnancy were not able to achieve stable emotional and sexual interpersonal relationships. One could assume, therefore, that the personality factors are more significant than the pregnancy itself. The majority of social factors seem to hold true for suicide attempts in pregnant women as well as those in nonpregnant women with only two exceptions; the pregnant women are slightly younger and are more often unmarried.

REFERENCES

1. Coppen, Alec: The biochemistry of affective disorders. *Brit. J. Psychiat.,* *113*:1237-1264, 1967.
2. Kallmann, Franz J.; De Porte, Joseph; De Porte, Elizabeth, and

Feingold, L.: Suicide in twins and only children. *Amer. J. Genet., 1*:113-126, 1949.

3. Stenstedt, Ake: Genetics of neurotic depression. *Acta Psychiat. Scand., 42*:392-409, 1966.

4. Dalton, Katharine: *The Premenstrual Syndrome.* Springfield, Thomas, 1964.

5. Mandell, Arnold J., and Mandell, Mary P.: Suicide and the menstrual cycle. *JAMA, 200*:792-793, 1967.

6. Tonks, C. M.; Rack, P. H., and Rose, M. J.: Attempted suicide and the menstrual cycle. *J. Psychosom. Res., 11*:319-323, 1968.

7. Whitlock, F. A., and Edwards, J. E.: Pregnancy and attempted suicide. *Compr. Psychiat., 9*:1-12, 1968.

8. Otto, Ulf: Suicide attempts by pregnant women under twenty-one years. *Acta Paedapsychiat. Scand., 32*:276-288, 1965.

Chapter VI
SUICIDE AND AGGRESSIVE BEHAVIOR

A RELATIONSHIP BETWEEN suicide and hostile aggressiveness, both from an individual as well as a cultural standpoint, has been considered by many writers.[1,2,3] Freud's[4] view was that suicide represented a turning inward of hostility from a hated and lost object to the self. Menninger[5] wrote that the suicidal person 1) wished to kill 2) wished to be killed, and 3) wished to die. Many studies of the behavior of suicidal patients would seem to corroborate these findings and demonstrate the presence of strong feelings of hostile aggression.

Some degree of aggression is present in every human being because it is necessary for survival. The amount of innate aggression varies with each individual. In addition, the amount of aggressive behavior can be increased both by frustration and exposure to repeated aggression in the environment. For example, some parents encourage and stimulate the overt expression of aggression within their children while other parents attempt to prohibit it. Frustration increases aggression whether it is provoked by the individual within the family unit or by the society in which he resides. How aggression is managed or even increased depends upon a multitude of circumstances for each child. One might say that the healthiest individual probably is born with a reasonable amount of innate aggressive potential and is taught by his family and his society to manage it well. On the other hand, there are children born with a larger amount of aggressive drive but even more important is the family or society which increases the amount of frustration and thus hostile aggression. In these cases there is usually a lack of reasonable training for the proper control of aggression. When the youngster reaches adolescence, aggressive drives normally increase and if these are already more than he can handle, he may well be headed toward difficulty.

Once we have an individual with excessive hostile, aggressive drives, he has two primary choices as to their outlet. He may turn them back upon himself in the form of self-destructive impulses or he may turn them outward towards others and attempt to destroy them. One can easily see the relatively close relationship between suicidal and homicidal impulses.

The authors have seen a few youngsters who have unusually great difficulty with aggression. These are children who are filled with pent-up rage as a result of their earlier upbringing. At the same time they have been so threatened by reprisal that the expression of this rage has forced them into a more passive but homosexual orientation. At the time of puberty and early adolescence their sexual and aggressive drives have increased, throwing their psychological equilibrium completely out of adjustment. They then would appear to have the choice of either going psychotic, becoming overtly homosexual, becoming suicidal or homicidal. In such youngsters one finds them almost experimenting with each mode of adjustment. They may on the one hand present transient effeminate features and then suddenly become depressed. This is soon replaced by active overt aggressive acts, and finally perhaps a psychotic episode.

HOMICIDE

A review of homicide statistics reveals that, like suicide, its incidence has been rising in both the ten to fourteen-year-old group as well as the fifteen to nineteen-year-old group. The increase in homicides in the older group is even more dramatic than the increase in suicides. Again one must remember that homicide represents the reverse of suicide, in that the aggressive impulses are directed outwardly toward the environment instead of toward the self. Suicide and homicide rates are often negatively correlated and thus represent one aspect of the relationship between the two. For example, we find that the suicide rate is higher in whites in comparison to nonwhites while the homicide rate is higher in nonwhites than in whites. Similarly the suicide rate is high and the homicide rate low for army officers while the reverse is true for enlisted men. The total incidence of suicide and homicide varies in different subcultures so that the combined suicide-homicide rate may really express the amount of aggression and violence in a particular area or cultural group.

It is not unusual for an individual to express both suicidal and homicidal impulses. For example, homicide followed by suicide is an unfortunate but not uncommon phenomenon reported in our newspapers. For example, a mother may kill her children and then herself, or a father may kill his children, his wife, and then himself. Studies of presidential assassinations or attempted assassinations frequently reveal strong suicidal attempts in the assassins.[6] Another example of the relationship between suicide and

TABLE III

PER 100,000 POPULATION

Homicide 15-19 Years of Age	1962	1963	1964	1965	1966	1967
General	3.7	3.6	4.3	4.3	5.1	6.1
Male	5.4	5.5	6.4	6.5	7.8	9.5
Female	1.9	1.7	2.2	2.1	2.4	2.6
White	1.9	2.0	2.2	2.2	2.5	2.9
Male	2.6	2.9	2.9	3.0	3.4	4.3
Female	1.3	1.0	1.4	1.3	1.6	1.6
Nonwhite	16.6	15.6	19.2	18.9	22.9	26.4
Male	27.0	25.0	30.9	30.8	38.0	43.8
Female	6.3	6.2	7.7	7.1	7.9	9.3

Taken from Vital Statistics of the United States, Volume 2, Mortality, United States Department of Health, Education and Welfare Public Health Service.

homicide is found among those patients who are admitted to a mental hospital on the basis of "a threat to kill" complaint. On follow-up study these individuals have been shown to have a high suicidal rate.[7] Psychiatrists and other mental health workers not infrequently encounter patients who ruminate about killing some specific individual while at the same time mention their own suicidal thoughts.

Case History: Helen

Helen was a seventeen-year-old girl when first seen by the psychiatrist. The history revealed that she had been adopted at age two by American parents when they were in a foreign country. On the surface it would have appeared that their motives for adopting this youngster were entirely altruistic. A more thorough evaluation revealed serious, neurotic factors contributing to the adoption. Both parents were extremely strict and unloving although they considered themselves model parents. They thought they had made a great sacrifice to adopt this child from a "bad background" and give her all their "love and attention." Needless to say the youngster became aware of their basic hostility early and much difficulty developed between her and her parents. By the time she was fifteen she made a suicide attempt by taking half a bottle of aspirin. During the psychiatric interview following this, it became evident that she had a strong antagonism to her parents but that aggression and hostility had never been permitted in the household. She had been expected to be grateful to her adoptive parents for having rescued her. She was really struggling with an intense desire to find an outlet for her hostility. Perhaps the most clear indication of the inability she had in determining the direction of her hostility came when she talked of the relationship with the family physician. On the one hand, she was extremely attached to and fond of him and in a sense had an adolescent "crush" on him. However, in her more disturbed moments she was bothered by an intense impulse to kill him.

AUTOMOBILE ACCIDENTS

The whole question of automobile accidents and their

relationship to suicidal impulses is as yet not fully understood. Quite obviously if one is bent upon suicide, an automobile offers a potential instrument to accomplish this. One need only achieve a high rate of speed and drive off the road or into a stone pillar. If one has the usual ambivalent question about whether or not to die, one may fortify oneself with alcohol, tranquilizers or some other form of medication and then perform the same act with the automobile. Often clues are left which allow experts in suicidology to assign a "suicidal" rather than "accidental" motive. If one is less aware of one's suicidal impulses it is quite possible to drive recklessly with or without alcohol or other pharmacological agents and sooner or later the odds are that one may be killed. Studies have shown that car accidents and suicide are related to the extent that persons with suicidal and/or homicidal impulses are more frequently involved in car accidents.[8] Adults with serious suicidal thoughts are twice as likely to have car accidents as adults without them.[9] MacDonald[10] has shown that in those cases of near-fatal accidents where a suicidal attempt was strongly suspected, the use of the car was an impulsive choice. In many instances such individuals have later suicided by other means. Freud, Menninger as well as others theorize that fatal and serious car accidents could represent atypical forms of suicide. Some authors[11,12] feel that the majority of car accidents do not represent unconscious suicide, but are acts which occur as a result of a particular type of character structure interacting with the environment. The character structure of high accident drivers has been described[13] as having poor control of hostility, poor tolerance for tension, high separation anxiety, and dependency needs with the extremes of egocentricity and sociocentricity. Such a description in a general kind of way characterizes adolescent behavior.

It would not come as any surprise to a reader who is the parent of a teen-age boy that insurance companies regard them as high risks. Interestingly enough this is not particularly true for young girls although some insurance companies have recently changed towards higher accident rates for girls also. There has been a steady increase in the number of car accidents in the fifteen to nineteen-year-old age group over the years. This increase is above and beyond the actual increase in the number of such drivers. Of greater significance, car accidents have been statistically correlated with the combined suicide-homicide rate of the community, suggesting that such accidents represent another aspect of the total violence and aggression seen within a community.[8]

The whole concept of the relationship of car accidents to suicidal impulses, as well as a possible extension to car accidents in the teen-age group bears further study. We know, for example, that many adolescents are relatively inexperienced and thus perhaps more prone to misjudgment. We also know that many of them are anxious to prove themselves to their peers and thus take unnecessary chances. It is also evident that the car represents to many, including a teen-ager, a sort of proof of power and it will be

TABLE IV

PER 100,000 POPULATION

Motor Vehicle Accidents 15-19 Years of Age	*1962*	*1963*	*1964*	*1965*	*1966*	*1967*
General	33.4	34.9	36.7	40.2	45.4	44.6
Male	50.2	52.3	54.7	61.0	67.3	66.7
Female	16.4	17.3	18.4	19.1	23.1	22.2
White	35.3	36.9	38.6	41.9	47.5	46.7
Male	53.1	55.1	57.5	63.5	70.4	69.7
Female	17.4	18.4	19.4	19.8	24.1	23.4
Nonwhite	21.8	23.9	23.0	28.7	31.2	30.7
Male	33.1	37.5	35.1	43.2	45.8	46.9
Female	10.6	10.5	11.2	14.3	16.6	14.6

Taken from Vital Statistics of the United States, Volume 2, Mortality, United States Department of Health, Education and Welfare Public Health Service.

used in accordance with the individual's own need to demonstrate power as well as his maturity or immaturity regarding the control of his own impulses. Important, however, is the fact that with the rise in teen-age suicides and homicides, there is a concomitant rise in automobile accidents among this age group. One can only assume there must be some correlation between these factors.

ACCIDENTAL OR "NORMAL EXPERIMENTATION?"

There is uncertainty regarding accidental or suicidal causation in a relatively small group of young adolescent boys who died by strangulation. These youngsters have certain things in common. The coroner's report often indicates that at the time of death they wore some piece of female clothing, were partially undressed, and had some signs of erotic stimulation.[14] One coroner reported that he saw approximately one case per year of such youngsters whose death was caused by some form of strangulation and whose genitals were encased in a plastic bag.[15] Stearns attempted to get retrospective data on these young boys and found that prior to their deaths they appeared to be well accepted in their neighborhoods and schools and he found no previous suicidal threats. Shankel[16] offers some explanation for this phenomenon in his report of an adolescent boy he saw in analysis. In his case report the boy obtained sexual stimulation from constriction of his neck. During these episodes he wore female clothing and masturbated. It would appear that perhaps these youngsters have transvestite tendencies although further study is needed. Possibly they have been struggling with a concept of sadomasochistic sex and while play acting it in a narcissistic way have "accidently" killed themselves.

REFERENCES

1. McCandless, Frederick D.: Suicide and the communication of

rage: a cross-cultural study. *Amer. J. Psychiat.*, *125*:197-205, 1968.

2. Eisenthal, Sherman: Suicide and aggression. *Psychol. Rep.*, *21*:745-751, 1967.

3. Lester, David: Suicide as an aggressive act. *J. Psychol.*, *66*:47-50, 1967.

4. Litman, Robert: Sigmund Freud on suicide. *Bull. Suicidology*, 11-23, 1968.

5. Menninger, Karl: *Man against Himself*. New York, Harcourt and Brace, 1956.

6. Weinstein, Edwin A., and Lyerly, Olga G.: Symbolic aspects of presidential assassinations. *Psychiatry, 32*:1-11, 1969.

7. MacDonald, John M.: Homicidal threats. *Amer. J. Psychiat.*, *124*:475-482, 1967.

8. Porterfield, Austin L.: Traffic fatalities, suicide and homicide. *Amer. Sociol. Rev., 25*:897-901, 1960.

9. Selzer, Melvin L., and Payne, Charles E.: Automobile accidents, suicide and unconscious motivation. *Amer. J. Psychiat., 119*:237-240, 1963.

10. MacDonald, John M.: Suicide and homicide by automobile. *Amer. J. Psychiat., 121*:366-370, 1964.

11. Tabachnick, Norman; Litman, Robert E.; Osman, Marvin; Jones, Warren L.; Cohn, Jay; Kasper, August, and Moffat, John: Comparative psychiatric study of accidental and suicidal death. *Arch. Gen. Psychiat., 14*:60-68, 1966.

12. Litman, Robert, and Tabachnick, Norman: Fatal one-car accidents. *Psychoanal. Quart. 36*:248-259, 1967.

13. Conger, John J.; Gaskill, Herbert S.; Glad, Donald D.; Hassel, Linda; Rainey, Robert V.; Sawrey, William L., and Turrell, Eugene J.: Psychological and psychophysiological factors in motor vehicle accidents. *JAMA, 169*:1581-1587, 1959.

14. Stearns, A. Warren: Cases of probable suicide in young persons without obvious motivation. *J. Maine Med. Ass., 44*:16-23, 1953.

15. Donovan, William B., and Nash, Gerald: Suicide rate: a problem of validity and comparability. *Marquette Med. Rev., 127*:150-158, 1962.

16. Shankel, L. Willard and Carr, Arthur C.: Transvestism and hanging episodes in a male adolescent. *Psychiat. Quart.,* *30*:478-493, 1956.

Chapter VII
SUICIDE IN COLLEGE STUDENTS

IN THE FALL OF every year, many thousands of late adolescents enter on a college career. Their number is increasing rapidly as is the size of many of the institutions they enter. They face a radical change of life circumstances from those of home and high school. Their motivations vary—some go because they have a clear awareness of education's relevance to their future goals, but others enter because their parents have pushed them or it seems the thing to do. Many certainly have only a faint comprehension of the struggles they will encounter in both academic and social life of college.

As we look at the statistics, it is not surprising that we find an increase in the suicide rate of the twenty to twenty-four-year-old group; an increase even more striking than in the younger age groups. There is some evidence that suicide in the college level population may be greater than in the general twenty to twenty-four-year-old age group. Studies done at the University of California,[1] Harvard,[2] and in British schools[3,4] point in this direction even though one study at Yale[5] shows an opposite trend. It is generally acceded that among college population, suicide ranks as the third leading cause of death, and even higher on some campuses.[6]

As one suspects, investigators have found differences in the suicide rate among different colleges and universities, with Ivy League colleges tending to have the higher rates and the smaller, less prestigious colleges the lower rates. A similar trend has been noted in England, in that we find Oxford and Cambridge reporting higher incidences

47

than the "red brick" universities.[1] However the epidemiological pattern suggests the operation of additional elements besides academic competition. The Ivy League college is often larger and less personal than its smaller counterpart, and some have questioned if the former attracts the bright but unstable student. In addition, among college students themselves, suicide is more frequent in the minority groups with an increased greater incidence of black undergraduates[4] and foreign students.[7]

There is no consistent pattern in the particular year of college the greatest number of suicides occur. For example, Harvard reports a higher incidence during the freshman year whereas Radcliff has a higher incidence in the sophomore and senior years.[2]

For every successful college suicide there are approximately fifty college students who attempt suicide. The latter group have been shown to have far more psychopathological disorders than those students who do not have suicidal impulses.[8] It is important to recognize that there is a greater difference between the suicidal and nonsuicidal student than between suicidal students with varying degrees of serious intent. In general, the suicidal students are more depressed, schizoid, and show obsessive-compulsive features in contrast to the nonsuicidal student.[9]

Some characteristics of the suicidal college student are relatively clear, while others are less so. Academically they may be poor, average, or even excellent students with a general tendency towards a higher than average grade point average. One study[7] demonstrated that while the suicidal undergraduate may have a generally high grade point average, it tended to fall in the final semester preceding the suicide attempt. This suggests that the emotional difficulties preceding this attempt could influence the student's ability to study. Or perhaps, depression and suicide were reactions to lower grades. Not infrequently, the suicidal college student is a social isolate. He is less likely to be athletic and more prone to be a nonparticipant in extra-curricular activities. He often is underweight and has an allergic predisposition.[10]

The family background of suicidal college students is not dissimilar from those of other adolescent suicides. These students come from families with a greater number of divorces, death of a parent, or separation from a parent during childhood. Two of these studies,[2,9] in addition, show that the families are more highly educated which might imply greater pressure for academic achievement in college.

The suicidal college student often demonstrates a change in his behavior prior to the suicide attempt. He is likely to be concerned over his studies as his academic performance begins to deteriorate. He will often go to the health service or to a physician with unusual physical symptoms, complaints of inability to eat or sleep or perhaps with a reported mood change. During this prodromal period, he becomes more asocial, withdrawn, and there is a distinct change in his interpersonal relationships. It therefore is important for the physician to take any suicidal threats by a college student seriously.

Such findings as have been described are not difficult to understand if one places oneself in the position of many young people going away to college for the first time. They may have done reasonably well in their local high schools from an academic and even possibly a social standpoint. They leave home for the first time with much pressure upon them to achieve in a large university. Their life is entirely different than it has been at home. They are no longer able to depend upon their parents in the way they once were. They are thrust into a new independence which they have felt they wanted, but do not know how to use. They are met with academic demands that are far greater than they have ever been subjected to before. They begin to worry about failures. They begin to socially isolate themselves and withdraw from most activities. In most uni-

versities, mental health help is at a premium and many do
not know how to seek it. Often when they do, their complaints are vague and difficult for the physician to decipher.
Mental health resource persons outside the university itself
may have little real understanding both of this age group
and the unique social pressures the student faces.

Case History: Carol

Carol was a freshman when she made a suicide attempt
by taking thirty aspirin. She planned this episode rather care-
fully in that she did not take the aspirin until she had tele-
phoned her boyfriend and alerted him that she was very
upset. It was only after he announced his intention to come
to see her immediately that she consumed the aspirin. While
the manipulative aspects of the suicide attempt were quite
transparent, the more basic self-destructive pattern in Carol's
personality was as evident.

Her past history revealed that Carol had had a very
stormy adolescence. At the age of thirteen she made her first
suicide attempt. The history revealed that this had apparently been primarily an attention-getting maneuver with little,
if any, demonstrable serious intent to kill herself. With the
onset of puberty her grades had dropped from above average
to near failing, despite an IQ in the superior range. Carol
began truanting from school, smoked on the school grounds,
and was involved in numerous altercations with other students and teachers. These activities culminated in her ex-
pulsion from school during her junior year. She was sent to a
private boarding school where she managed to complete her
academic work, but was lonely and depressed. She felt iso-
lated from and rejected by her friends and her family.

The family pattern strongly promoted higher education
for all the children and both of Carol's older brothers as well
as her younger sister attended college. Following their pattern, Carol completed boarding school, returned home, and
remained there while attending college. She continued to
maintain a reasonable academic average but her underlying
emotional conflicts remained unresolved. Her powerful sadomasochistic orientation was perhaps most evident in her relationships with boyfriends. She would bait them incessantly

testing them in a cruel fashion often to the point where they would become physically abusive to her. Any boy who failed to respond as she wished would be dropped. Since she was an attractive youngster, many boys were initially attracted to her, but she was incapable of forming any sort of mature, intimate, or satisfying relationship with any of them.

Carol's excessive narcissism revealed itself in her constant concern with her appearance. She spent inordinate amounts of time and energy on her appearance and was exceedingly sensitive to any slight imperfections in her complexion, her hair, or her figure. While some of this behavior is not uncommon in early adolescence, it was excessive in Carol's case and indicative of considerable immaturity.

Fortunately, Carol was able to enter psychotherapy and make reasonably good use of it. She worked through many of her emotional immaturities and began to relate on a much more age appropriate level. She managed to successfully complete her college career and at last report had a fairly stable relationship with a young man which had lasted for more than a year. Her earlier suicidal behavior had been a clear index of her emotional difficulties but in both attempts there had been little real intent for death.

When this type of suicidal attempt does actually succeed, it is usually because they are a misjudgment. Either the medicine proves more lethal than anticipated or the expected help does not arrive as they had assumed.

Case History: Paul

Paul, an eighteen-year-old undergraduate student in a small eastern college, was referred to the mental health clinic from the student health service. His chief complaint was that of insomnia. He was a tall, slender youth with a sallow complexion and glasses who spoke in a clipped decisive manner. His appearance was neat almost to the point of meticulousness. He was annoyed and resentful at having been referred to the psychiatrist and called the referring physician "nuts." While he admitted to having had difficulty sleeping, he said that tranquilizers had given him relief. He ascribed his insomnia to "an overactive brain." By this he meant that he mulled through many things in an obsessional manner during the process of trying to go to sleep. While lying in bed he would make long lists of things that he should do the next day. He expressed two somatic concerns. The first was that he was losing his hair which he rationalized as "the male type of baldness." He also complained of skin irritation on his scrotum which he had attempted to cure by scrubbing with a brush, aggravating the condition. As he left the first interview, the psychiatrist suggested that he make the next appointment when he himself wished to come.

Three months later, Paul returned and said that he was in difficulty academically. He was also worried about an increase in his insomnia. He appeared interested in getting psychiatric help and his attitude was no longer arrogant. He was still spending inordinate amounts of time at night meditating about what he should be doing the next day. He then made weekly visits to the psychiatrist during the next month, but was unable to really involve himself emotionally in treatment. His mood fluctuated during these visits. While at times he was mildly depressed, he was never seriously so, and gave no indication that he had any suicidal thoughts or intentions. During his treatment hours, he discussed his concerns about school and the fact that he could not absorb the material presented nor pay attention in class. He found himself particularly unable to pick out relevant data from the mass of material presented in classes.

Paul was an extremely compulsive individual. He talked about his roommate whom he felt had feminine mannerisms. He himself was sexually inhibited and dated only rarely. He gave no evidence of overt homosexuality although latent trends in this direction seemed apparent.

Paul mentioned only a few incidents from his childhood. At the age of nine, he lost most of the sight of one eye when he was tinkering with the machinery in his father's workshop. An opthalmologist had indicated that contact lenses would improve his vision but he had what he called "a mental block" against using them. He had been enuretic until age fourteen. During high school, he had felt awkward at sports, he had been average academically, but had constantly worried about relationships with his peers.

The few comments he made about his parents were for the most part factual, and revealed little emotion. While he seemed fond of them, his statements lacked real affect. He described his father as a "self-made man" who drove himself and others. He mentioned several times that his father put little stock in psychiatry. His mother had been raised by relatives following the death of her parents early in her life. Although he described her as a more emotionally mature person than his father, it appeared that he really had little close relationship with either parent.

On his fourth and last visit, Paul said he would prefer to withdraw from school, return home, and seek further psychiatric help. After the arrangements for this were discussed, Paul left the interview feeling enthusiastic about his decision. A few days later he called to express his concern about his draft status. Two days later he was found dead in his apartment. He had committed suicide by hanging himself. The remainder of the picture became somewhat clearer during the subsequent weeks.

Paul's parents sent a friend of the family with a letter giving their permission to handle his affairs along with a list of instructions of what should be done. The parents asked that all of his personal belongings be given to charity. They did not want anything connected with their son to be returned to their home. The friend of the family who carried out these instructions had with him some letters exchanged by Paul and his parents. In these letters, the father appeared as a brash, forceful man who openly distained weakness or helplessness. He sometimes wrote that good grades were not everything while at other times he upbraided his son for not having sufficiently high academic marks. The mother's letters reproved her son for his laziness, selfishness, and lack of concern for others, followed by apologetic notes. The true intensity of this young boy's conflicts with his parents and their merciless rejection of him was not recognized until after his death.

REFERENCES

1. Bruyn, Henry B., and Seiden, Richard H.: Student suicide: fact or fantasy? *Amer. Coll. Health Ass., 14*:250-256, 1966.
2. Blaine, Graham B., and Carmen, Lida A.: Causal factors in suicidal attempts by male and female college student. *Amer. J. Psychiat., 125*:146-149, 1968.

3. Parnell, R. W., and Scottowe, Ian: Towards preventing suicide. *Lancet, 272*:206-208, 1957.
4. Rook, Alan: Student suicide. *Brit. Med. J., 1*:599-603, 1959.
5. Parrish, Henry M.: Epidemiology of suicide among college students. *Yale J. Biol. Med., 29*:585-595, 1957.
6. Peck, Michael: Suicide motivations in adolescents. *Adolescence, 3*:109-118, 1968.
7. Seiden, Richard H.: Campus tragedy: a study of student suicide. *J. Abnorm. Psychol., 71*:389-399, 1966.
8. Braaten, Leif J., and Darling, C. Douglas: Suicidal tendencies among college students. *Psychiat Quart., 36*:665-692, 1962.
9. Braaten, Leif J.: Some reflections on suicide tendencies among college students. *Ment. Hyg., 47*:562-568, 1963.
10. Paffenbarger, Ralph S., and Asnes, Daniel P.: Chronic disease in former college students. *Amer. J. Public Health, 56*:1026-1036, 1966.

Chapter VIII

ASSESSMENT AND MANAGEMENT OF SUICIDAL BEHAVIOR

THE POTENTIAL SUICIDAL adolescent may come to the attention of the physician or other professional under a variety of different conditions. This will range all the way from the doctor in the emergency room who must resort to lifesaving measures for an adolescent who has made a serious suicidal attempt to the school social worker who detects a note of potential suicide in a teen-ager's conversation. It is, therefore, important that some knowledge about possible future suicidal behavior becomes a part of the practice of all of these individuals. It is not uncommon that suicidal threats, gestures, or even attempts are either ignored or not dealt with realistically by even the professional mental health worker. Many physicians do everything in their power to avoid potentially suicidal patients. Perhaps this is akin to the avoidance of psychotic patients by some professionals because such tendencies are deeply feared and repressed by all of us. To face and to interview a patient who is becoming psychotic is not particularly easy. Similarly to face and to interview the in-patient who talks about suicidal ideas can be equally difficult.

RECOGNITION OF SUICIDAL POTENTIAL

While no physician is capable of detecting and preventing all future suicides, it is important that he be alerted to various signs and symptoms which will increase his recognition of suicidal potential and thus his ability to deal with it effectively.

Depression, while still a valuable sign of possible suicidal intent, is seen less consistently in adolescents than in adults. the teen-ager usually does not say he is depressed, but may talk about feeling sad, blue, or "turned off." He may verbalize a chronic feeling of despair. Some of these patients resort to somatic equivalents of depression such as insomnia, fatigue, loss of appetite, and libido although they are less useful in adolescents than adults. More frequently they may complain about an inability to concentrate.

Sometimes meaningless activity, frequently an unusual style of behavior for a particular adolescent, provides an escape from impending depressive feelings. Running away from home is one of the more frequent "escape" activities.

The overtly psychotic suicidal adolescent is usually the easiest to recognize. For example, there is the extreme case where the patient says that voices are commanding him to kill himself. More difficult to identify as a possible suicide is the adolescent who is paranoid. He tends to be quiet, withdrawn, and refuses to divulge his fantasy life. In general, every psychotic adolescent should be thought of as potentially suicidal until he is well enough understood to rule this possibility out.

Any suicidal threat or attempt on the part of the teen-ager should be taken seriously. For example, the teen-ager who writes a school theme in which suicidal thoughts are evident deserves thorough evaluation. In other instances the youngster will leave a suicidal note where it will be found by a member of the family. Obviously not all such youngsters are seriously intent upon killing themselves but the healthy teen-ager does not dwell upon these themes. Some suicidal notes, gestures and essays are merely manipulative attempts on the part of the adolescent, but some are not. Each case certainly deserves full evaluation.

The past history of these youngsters will usually provide valuable information which must be included in the total assessment of the patient. For example, there is an increased risk of suicide if a patient, guardian, or "important" relative died during the patient's earlier years. Such a loss enhances the possibility of suicide by the patient who has identified with the loved but lost person. Particularly in younger patients, suicide can in these instances constitute an attempt at a "reunion." The term "a death trend" has been used to label some families, in which death has tended to occur under traumatic and sometimes tragic circumstances, often in more than one generation. A past history which includes a family history of mental illness, emotional problems or epilepsy does not have direct significance for possible suicide.

Whenever the physician feels there are possible suicidal trends in an adolescent it is quite appropriate that he ask the youngster if he ever thought of harming himself. Many patients would honestly answer such a question and make the whole treatment plan much easier to formulate. To the youngster who has not had serious suicidal thoughts such a question is responded to by a qualified "No." Since most people have had thoughts of suicide at one time or another, a complete denial has little meaning. The teenager preoccupied with suicidal thoughts is often relieved that the physician brings the question into the open and allows him to discuss it. An adolescent may reply that he has thought of harming himself but would never do so. This answer cannot be relied upon. The physician must be able to evaluate the answer given by the adolescent both in verbal content and emotional involvement. This, in turn, can be evaluated within the context of his total life situation.

EVALUATION OF THE SUICIDE ATTEMPT

Whenever the physician or other professional is called upon to evaluate an adolescent who has actually attempted suicide he should be prepared to allot sufficient time to obtain all the necessary information. He should be appraised of the details of the suicide attempt itself. He should have a full knowledge of the teen-ager's background and also a thorough knowledge of the family. It is only after obtaining all of this information that the physician can begin to evaluate the degree of seriousness of the suicidal act.

It should be remembered that in many instances the family will tend to negate the importance of such an attempt and in other instances the patient himself will minimize the seriousness of his intent. By denying a serious suicide intent, the emotional problems behind the suicide are avoided. There are some objective criteria for evaluating the seriousness of intent, although these can never be relied upon completely. For example, the method used in the suicide attempt is important. The more serious the intent, the more dangerous means of suicide will probably be employed. These would include such things as leaping from a high place, shooting one's self, or running in front of an oncoming car. Any method which is cruel or bizarre usually implies serious psychopathological disorders. For example, swallowing of foreign bodies is usually found only in those youngsters who are seriously disturbed. The same thing could be said of those teen-agers who arrange multiple means to accomplish death.

It is a reasonable but not infallible truism that the majority of suicide attempts which are arranged to be discovered are not serious. Discreet questioning will often reveal that the patient gave considerable thought to making his suicide attempt in a fashion which would quickly come to the attention of family members or close friends. Certainly the fact that other people are nearby when the attempt is made is not in itself evidence of whether the intent was serious or not. For example, the "exhibitionistic type" of suicide such as perching on a ledge of a high building before an audience is often done by those with deep-seated suicidal drives and psychosis is often an integral part of the picture.

It should be borne in mind that any suicidal attempt which includes an attempt to kill another person is always serious. Similarly, if in the suicidal attempt there is demonstrated extreme impulsiveness or the opposite, namely minute preparation, a more serious attempt can be suspected.

The reaction of the patient following an unsuccessful suicide attempt may give some hint of the seriousness. If, for example, the patient seems relieved and grateful it would appear less serious, but if he is sullen, downcast or enraged, it is likely that he is a poor risk in terms of future suicidal attempts.

Merely because the patient appears superficially improved does not mean that all suicide risk is dissolved. The psychiatrist faces the possibility that, after the initial recovery from the suicidal attempt, a patient who seems on the upswing and apparently a good candidate for discharge from the hospital may in fact be a prime candidate for another suicidal attempt.

MANAGEMENT OF A SUICIDE ATTEMPT

The whole problem of hospitalization of the adolescent who has attempted suicide is a complex one. Not infrequently such a youngster is first seen in the emergency room of a general hospital. The attempt itself may have been of such a nature as to not require hospitalization, but perhaps only a few simple medical procedures. The question then usually arises as to whether the adolescent should be allowed to return home, be hospitalized in the general hospital, or if available, placed in a psychiatric unit. All too frequently an overworked emergency room staff will return such a youngster home with vague directions that he and his parents seek psychiatric guidance on an out-patient basis in the not too distant future.

We feel that every adolescent who makes a suicide

attempt should have a thorough psychiatric examination. There are, of course, areas in which psychiatric consultation is essentially unavailable and under these conditions the evaluation will have to be done either by someone else in the mental health field or by the general physician himself. Unfortunately, in our country today with the rising number of emotionally disturbed and even suicidal adolescents there is a serious shortage of psychiatric beds available to them. This may mean that a teen-ager who is potentially seriously suicidal may have to remain at home even though it would be preferable if he were hospitalized.

The physician has a responsibility to discuss with the family the possible suicidal risks as he perceives them to exist. Quite frequently, if out-patient psyciatric treatment can be arranged, the suicidal risks will be diminished but this is not always true. Certainly the family should take reasonable precautions to remove lethal medication, guns, and other such suicidal instruments from the home. In many instances environmental manipulation by the physician may lesson some of the stresses and strains on the adolescent and thus diminish suicidal potential. For example, a change in school curriculum, a working out of a better understanding between the teen-ager and his parents, or an opportunity for the youngster to discuss troublesome matters with a physician, perhaps even with his parents, are all examples of steps that can be taken. In those instances, in which the home situation seems to be unchangeable and at the same time contributing to the adolescent's problems, it may be wise for him to live, at least temporarily, elsewhere. A group placement or a relative's home may suffice in such instances depending on the type of problem and availability of a placement.

PRESCRIPTION OF POTENTIALLY LETHAL DRUGS

The use of drugs over other means of suicide has increased disproportionately in recent years.[1] Since many of the drugs used in suicidal attempts are available only by prescription, the physician can exert some control in this area. Perhaps the most common exception is aspirin which is often used by adolescents in their suicidal attempts. It is fortunate that the majority of those teenagers who utilize aspirin in their suicide attempts are not serious in their intent to die. Barbiturates are used approximately thirty-two times more often than tranquilizers in suicides despite the fact that equal amounts of both kinds of drugs are being prescribed.[1] Barbiturates, particularly phenobarbital, can produce or intensify preexisting depression and suicidal tendencies. It would therefore seem wise that barbiturates should not be prescribed for suicidal patients.

In prescribing medication for the potentially suicidal patient, the physician should exercise caution in regard to the amount of the drug in each prescription. It is useful, for the doctor to be aware of the ratio of the average daily dose of the particular medication to the massive dose. The latter is defined as a dose which produces clinical symptoms which may be dangerous but not necessarily fatal. A decision as to what constitutes a massive dose is often arbitrary. There are some psychotherapeutic drugs which have a wide dosage range particularly when one takes into account such factors as age, sex, and the physical status of the patient. Nevertheless, some rough guidelines are helpful. For instance, a thirty day supply of most major or minor tranquilizers is reasonably safe with the exception of meprobamate. With the latter drug, as well as the antidepressant group, a ten-day supply is relatively safe. Barbiturates should not be prescribed for more than one week's supply. A massive dose of barbiturates is only about ten to fifteen times the average hypnotic dose and, therefore, even a two week's supply could constitute a massive dose.

If a patient is seriously suicidal even the most careful caution on the part of the physician in writing prescriptions may be to no avail. Such patients tend to save up their medication until they have accumulated a lethal amount. Even hospitalized patients not infrequently resort to this method even when the medication is dispensed in what would appear to be an extremely careful manner. A capsule can be kept hidden under the tongue only to be removed after the nurse is no longer watching.

It would appear that the widespread use of major tranquilizers in schizophrenia has not directly contributed to an increase in suicides in this group of patients.[2] An occasional psychotic patient who is given major tranquilizers may improve symptomatically and then be given too much responsibility too rapidly. A decompensation may then occur with subsequent suicide.

PROGNOSIS

Some statistics have been accumulated chiefly from adult populations which are predictive of future suicidal activity. One of the more important indicators is a history of previous suicide attempt particularly if that attempt resulted in unconsciousness. It would appear, however, that there is not a measurable increase in risk between the first and second attempts.[3] However, one study of adults revealed a substantially increased risk after three suicide attempts.[4] A history of previous psychiatric hospitalization increases the possibility of future suicidal behavior. One study[5] of adolescents who were hospitalized for a suicide attempt revealed that 40 per cent made subsequent attempts. Statistically, in this population the adolescent who lived away from his family was more likely to make repeated suicide attempts than the adolescent who returned home. This probably reflects the long-term effects of family instability and therefore is not a useful guidepost in management. As mentioned previously, the loss of a parent during early childhood increases the possibility of not only initial but repeated suicide behavior. While poor school performance is found in adolescents who attempt suicide, as a whole, school performance after the initial attempt cannot be used prognostically. On the other hand, an adequate social life appears to be a reasonable indicator for decreased suicidal behavior after a suicide attempt. There are no statistics available for adolescents who are psychotic, but one could assume that they form a more serious risk group. Certainly, in adults who have attempted suicide, the psychotics tend to make more serious attempts and the completion rate is much higher.

Although, as mentioned above, there is considerable evidence that anyone who attempts suicide is more likely to kill himself in the future than the individual who never made such an attempt, the situation is somewhat more complex than it might appear. For example, based on studies of an adult population[6] a successful suicide in the future cannot be predicted on the degree of "seriousness" of the suicidal attempt. Again follow-up studies on adult populations of attempted suicide demonstrate that the longer the original population was followed, the higher the incidence of completed suicide.[7] It is not known whether these figures from adult studies would hold equally true for the adolescent group. It is known that the proportion of adolescents who attempt suicide compared to the number who complete suicide is much higher in the adolescent group than in the adult. Only very long-term studies would suffice to answer some of these questions.

REFERENCES

1. Berger, F. M.: Drugs and suicide in the United States. *Clin Pharmacol. Ther., 8*:219-223, 1967.
2. Cohen, Sidney,; Leonard, Calista V.; Farberow, Norman, and Schneidman, Edwin: Tranquilizers and suicide in the schizophrenic patient. *Arch. Gen. Psychiat., 11*:312-321, 1964.
3. Tuckman, Jacob; Youngman, William F., and Kriezman, Garry: Multiple suicide attempts. *Comm. Ment. Health J., 4*:164-170, 1968.

4. Ettlinger, Ruth W.: Suicides in a group of patients who had previously attempted suicide. *Acta Psychiat. Scand., 40*:363-378, 1964.

5. Barter, James T.; Swaback, Dwight O., and Todd, Dorothy: Adolescent suicide attempts: a follow-up study of hospitalized patients. *Arch. Gen. Psychiat., 19*:523-527, 1968.

6. Cohen, Earl; Motto, Jerome A., and Seiden, Richard H.: An instrument for evaluating suicide potential: a preliminary study. *Amer. J. Psychiat., 122*:886-891, 1966.

7. Dorpat, Theodore L., and Ripley, Herbert J.: The relationships between attempted suicide and committed suicide. *Comp. Psychiat., 8*:74-79, 1967.

INDEX